Nature Yearbook

Nature Yearbook

Colour Library Direct

© 1998 Children's Leisure Products Limited, David Dale House,
New Lanark, ML11 9DJ, Scotland.

Written and designed by arrangement with Simon Girling & Associates.

Artwork by Elizabeth Sawyer
CLD 21285
This edition published 1999 for Colour Library Direct
by Geddes & Grosset, an imprint of Children's Leisure Products Limited.

Colour Library Direct,
Godalming Business Centre,
Woolsack Way Godalming,
Surrey GU7 1 XW

ISBN 1-84100-040-X

Printed and bound in Singapore.

Introduction

The British Isles contain a surprising variety of flora and fauna. Some are evident, or at their best, only in certain seasons of the year.

This yearbook gives a charming, beautifully illustrated representation of the wildlife of rural Britain as it appears in the unfolding months. It depicts many of the animals, birds, insects, plants and scenery that accompany the changing seasons.

As well as being a functional diary for any year, this book leaves space to give you the opportunity to make your own daily notes and record general observations regarding the wildlife in your area.

January

1

2

3

4

5

6

7

A snow-covered country road

January

Snowdrops were once rare in Britain, found only in the damp woodlands of western England. Today, they still make a welcome sight, flowering as they do during the hostile months of January through to March.

January

8

9

10

11

12

13

14

Long-tailed tit

January

15

16

17

18

19

20

21

January

The first yellow flower of the new year, the winter aconite, opens its glossy petals in the January sunshine.

Wintering birds

Great tit

Long-tailed tit

Green woodpecker

Brambling

12

22
_____

23
_____

24
_____

25
_____

26
_____

27
_____

28
_____

January

29

30

31

Oak marble gall

Notes

February

1

2

3

4

5

6

7

An estuary at dusk

Female shelduck and chicks

February

8

9

10

11

12

13

14

The avocet is very rare and is usually only to be found in the reserves in East Anglia, where it breeds, or in estuaries in the southwest of England.

February

15

16

17

18

19

20

21 Seeds . Planted. Dahlias.
Stocks.
Mon. Basil
cup&saucer.
Blue tits. 1 pair of Siskins. Blackbirds, 1 Robin.
Starlings.

Winter crocus

February

22

23

24

25

26

27

28

29

The hardy little crocus is a flower that
can survive the bitter frost and snow
which sometimes persists into the
beginning of the British spring.

Notes

March

1

2

3

4

5

6

7

Ploughing the fields for the new crop

March

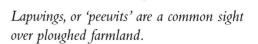

A nesting chiffchaff

Lapwings, or 'peewits' are a common sight over ploughed farmland.

The lapwing lays its well camouflaged eggs in a simple 'solape' in the earth.

8

9

10

11

12

13

14

March

15

16

17

18

19

20

21

Sweet violet

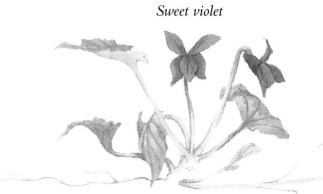

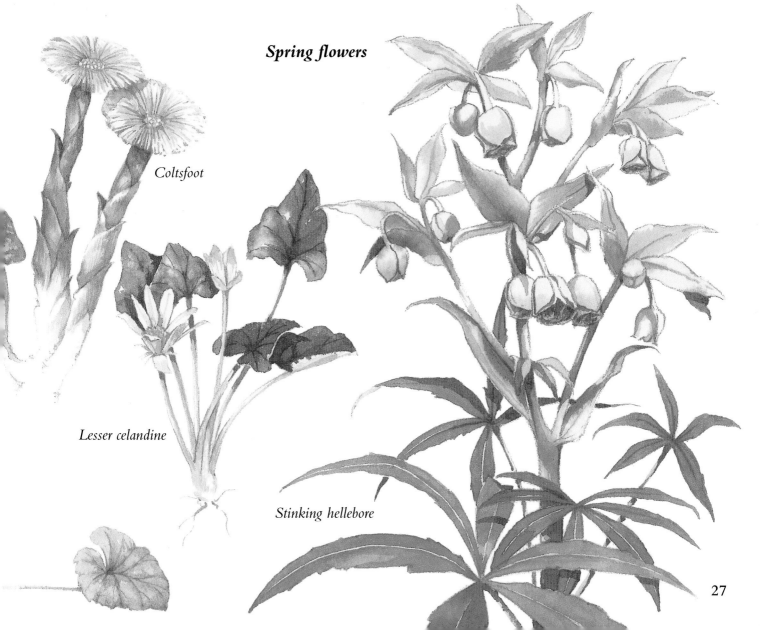

Spring flowers

Coltsfoot

Lesser celandine

Stinking hellebore

27

22

23

24

25

26

27

28

Daffodils are amongst the first of the spring flowers to appear after the long winter.

March

29

30

31

Depending on the area of the country, lambing very often takes place in early spring.

Notes

April

1

2

3

4

5

6

7

A pond with grasses, reeds and water lilies

Frog spawn

The common frog can be found throughout Britain and
Ireland – its usual habitat being damp vegetation near water.
It is a very well camouflaged creature, with speckled skin
that can vary in colour from greenish-grey, through bright
yellow, to dark olive-brown.

34

8

9

10

11

12

13

14

April

15

16

17

18

19

20

21

Cowslip

Primrose

22

23

24

25

26

27

28

The arum's fertilized female flowers develop into highly poisonous, blood-red berries.

Wild arum is a common, albeit exotic-looking, plant of British woods and hedgerows. Its delicate green spathes, with a slight odour of decay, invite insects to pollinate the female flowers.

Arum is also affectionately known as Lords and Ladies. Other, less majestic names include Adam and Eve, sweethearts and cuckoo pint.

April

29

30

Wood sorrel

Notes

May

1

2

3

4

5

6

7

A woodland of wild garlic

May

8

9

10

11

12

13

14

Bluebells, yellow archangel,
and stitchwort combine to form
this stunning hedgerow display.

May

15

19

16

20

17

21

18

Spring butterflies

Green hairstreak

Orange tip

Pearl-bordered fritillary

Common blue

Speckled wood

47

The luxuriant marsh marigold, or king cup, can be seen brightening the ditches, wet meadows and shady places of the countryside, from March to July. Also known as May blobs, it used to be hung upside down in doorways to ward off witches.

May

22

23

24

25

26

27

28

Wood sorrel

May

29

_____

30

_____

31

_____

Notes

June

1

2

3

4

5

6

7

The seashore in summer

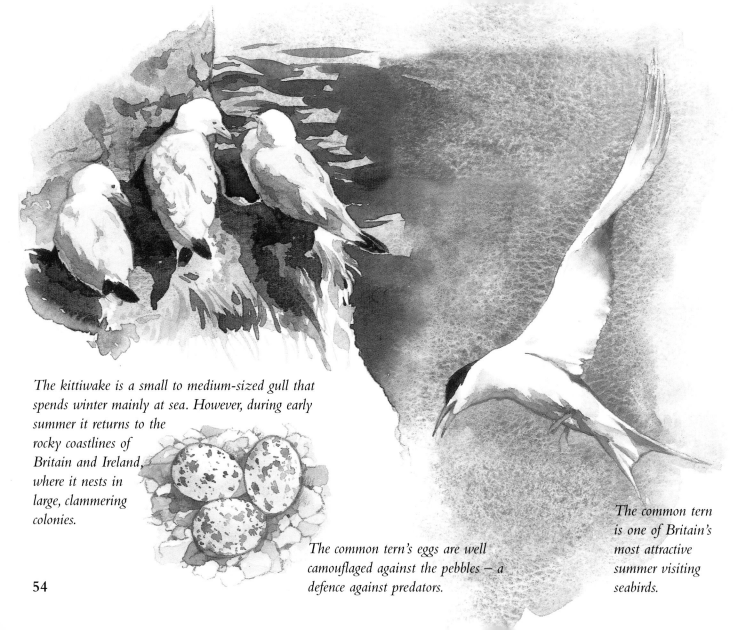

The kittiwake is a small to medium-sized gull that spends winter mainly at sea. However, during early summer it returns to the rocky coastlines of Britain and Ireland, where it nests in large, clammering colonies.

The common tern's eggs are well camouflaged against the pebbles – a defence against predators.

The common tern is one of Britain's most attractive summer visiting seabirds.

54

8

9

10

11

12

13

14

June

15

16

17

18

19

20

21

June

The shore crab can be found hiding under
stones and among seaweed all along the
coasts of Britain, and even in some
estuaries. Its shell is usually dark green,
but the underside is of a glowing
orange-red colour.

*Greater
butterfly
orchid*

*Pyramidal
orchid*

*Bee
orchid*

58

Downland orchids

Common
spotted
orchid

Fragrant
orchid

Ever since Henry VII adopted the Tudor rose as his emblem, the dog rose, the ancestor of all garden roses, has been synonymous with England and all that is English. With its delicate pink flowers, it brightens the hedgerows and scrublands of England and Wales between June and July.

22

23

24

25

26

27

28

Honeysuckle, also known as woodbine, is a vigorous climbing plant familiar in woods and hedgerows. On a summer's evening, the sweet fragrance of the honeysuckle fills the air.

June

_____

29

_____

30

_____

Marbled white butterfly

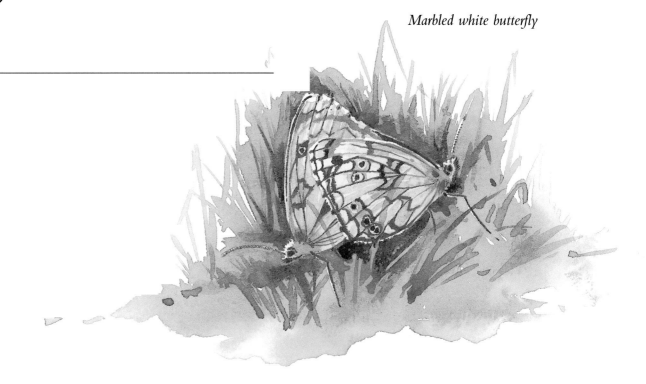

Notes

July

1

2

3

4

5

6

7

The tranquility of the riverside in summer

July

8

9

10

11

12

13

14

Despite its bright colouring, the kingfisher is sometimes difficult to spot on the riverbank – its plumage perhaps merging with the rich variety of summer flora. The sound of its shrill, trilling call or the splash of the bird catching a small fish may be the best indication of its presence.

July

15

16

17

18

19

20

21

Nymphaea alba, *one of the most beautiful of the white water lilies, flowers from June to August in sheltered ponds.*

July

22 _____

23 _____

24 _____

25 _____

26 _____

27 _____

28 _____

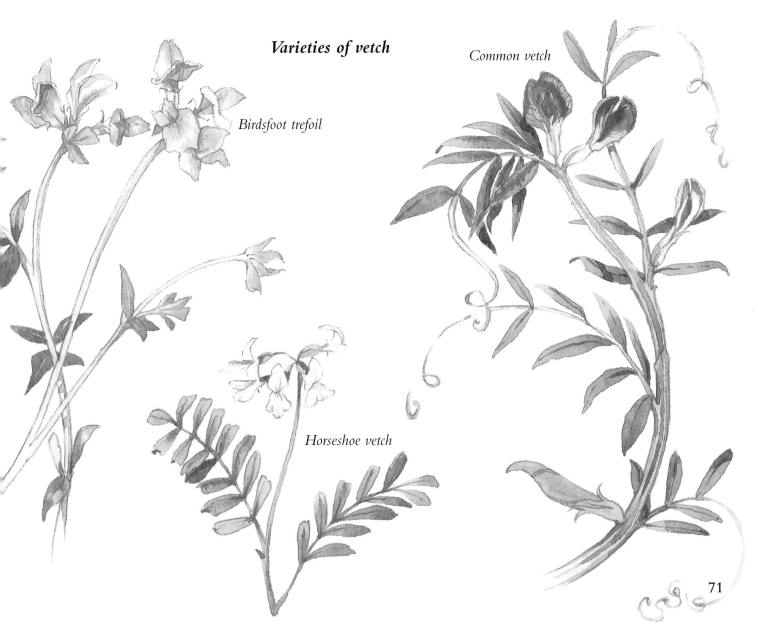

Varieties of vetch

Common vetch

Birdsfoot trefoil

Horseshoe vetch

71

July

29
_____

30
_____

31
_____

_____

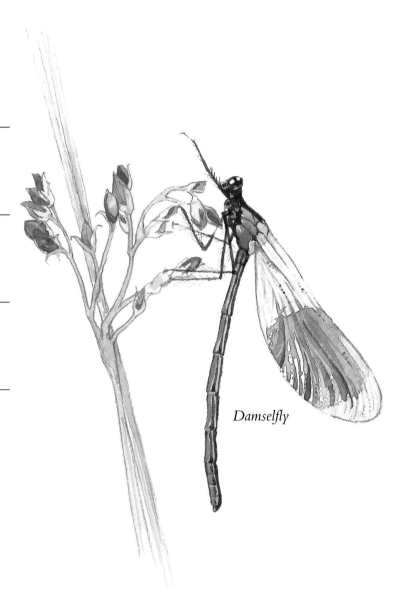

Damselfly

Notes

August

1

2

3

4

5

6

7

Heathland in late summer

August

8

9

10

11

12

13

14

Primarily a bird of heathlands, the stonechat is usually seen perching on a high vantage point, such as a bush or telegraph wire, scolding with it's distinctive 'wheet, sack-sack' call. It feeds mainly on insects and other small creatures.

Grayling

Emperor moth

August

15

16

17

18

19

20

21

August

22

23

24

25

26

27

28

A family of adders: the male is paler in colour than the copper-brown female. On warm summer days, these beautiful reptiles emerge to bask in the sun. Perhaps their most distinctive feature, is their large, red eyes with vertical pupils – a sure sign of a venomous snake.

August

_____

29

_____

30

_____

31

_____

*The sticky leaves of the
sundew plant mean certain
death to any unsuspecting
insect.*

Notes

September

1

2

3

4

5

6

7

Red deer

September

8

9

10

11

12

13

14

Wood mice

September

15

16

17

18

19

20

21

Red admiral butterfly

Autumn fruits

The flowers of the elder are used to make wine
and 'champagne'. In the autumn, the berries
also make excellent wine and jam.

Rosehips, the fruits of the dog rose, are rich in vitamin C, and are well known for their medicinal properties. They are most commonly made into rosehip syrup.

Probably the best known of all the hedgerow fruits, blackberries make superb jellies, jam, pies and wine.

89

Once, when cereal crops were harvested by hand, the harvest mouse's ball-like nest was a common sight, tenuously attached to the cornfield stalks. However, since the advent of the combine harvester, this delightful little mouse is now a rare creature in the fields.

September

22

23

24

25

26

27

28

September

___

29

___

30

___

Wild rabbits

Notes

October

1

2

3

4

5

6

7

October

8

9

10

11

12

13

14

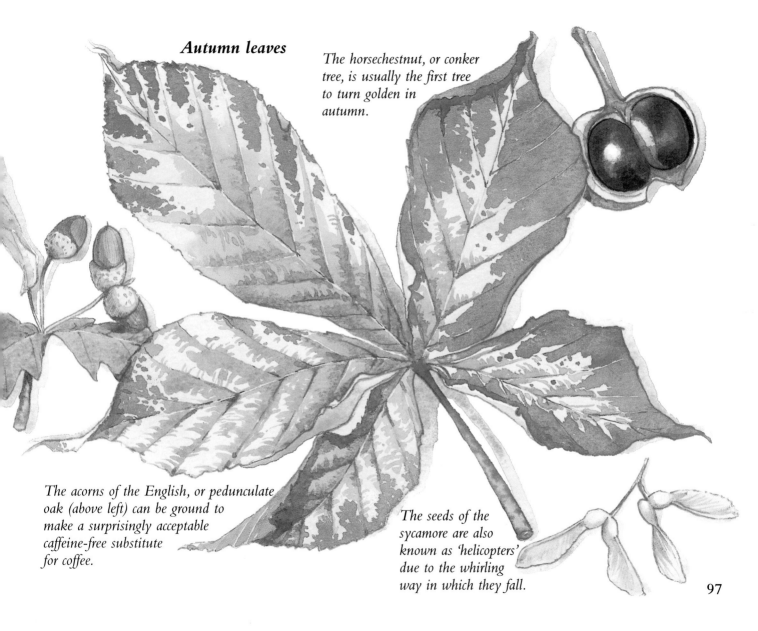

Autumn leaves

The horsechestnut, or conker tree, is usually the first tree to turn golden in autumn.

The acorns of the English, or pedunculate oak (above left) can be ground to make a surprisingly acceptable caffeine-free substitute for coffee.

The seeds of the sycamore are also known as 'helicopters' due to the whirling way in which they fall.

October

15

16

17

18

19

20

21

Wood blewitt mushrooms

22

23

24

25

26

27

28

Pine cone

October

29

30

31

Wood mice

Notes

November

1

2

3

4

5

6

7

The bare branches of woodlands in late autumn

November

8

9

10

11

12

13

14

Garden snails are widespread throughout the British Isles, mostly feeding on leaves and fruit. They are common occupants of our gardens, though often the first indication of their presence is their silvery slime trails.

15

16

17

18

19

20

21

Robin

November

22

23

24

25

26

27

28

The fly agaric is one of Britain's most colourful, but poisonous, fungi. During late summer to late autumn, the floor of the birch woods can be carpeted with these beautiful, vibrant red mushrooms.

107

November

29

30

Wood blewitt mushrooms

Notes

December

1

2

3

4

5

6

7

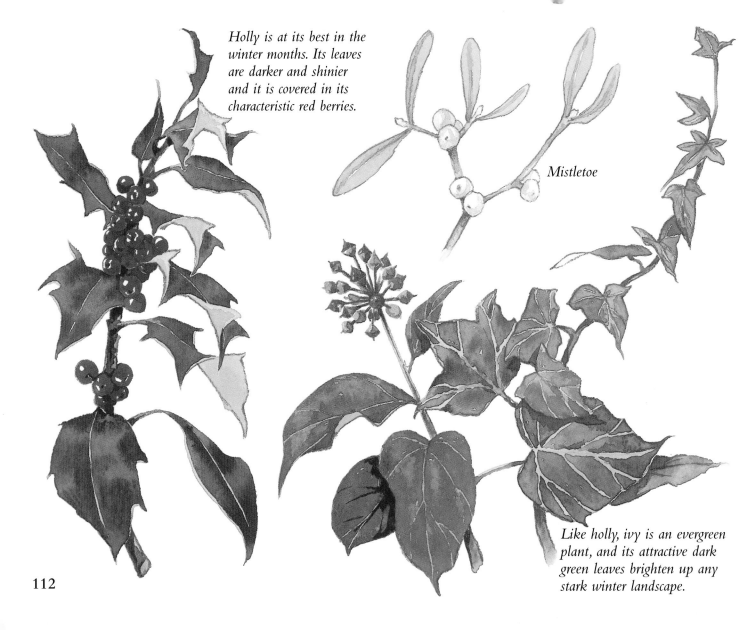

Holly is at its best in the winter months. Its leaves are darker and shinier and it is covered in its characteristic red berries.

Mistletoe

Like holly, ivy is an evergreen plant, and its attractive dark green leaves brighten up any stark winter landscape.

112

December

8

12

9

13

10

14

11

The custom of stealing a kiss from anyone who stands beneath the mistletoe is said to derive from the plant's parasitic freedom to grow upon any tree or bush.

December

15

16

17

18

19

20

21

A fox in winter

December

22

23

24

25

26

27

28

December

29

30

31

The red-breasted robin is a familiar sight in the
winter garden. Its song is more varied and its
plumage richer and brighter in autumn and
winter than at any other time of the year.

Notes

Index

Index

List of Flora and Fauna

Adder	Vipera berus
Avocet	Recurvirostra avosetta
Bee orchid	Ophrys apifera
Birdsfoot trefoil	Lotus corniculatus
Blackberry	Rubus fruticosus
Bluebell	Endymion non-scriptus
Brambling	Fringilla montifringilla
Chiffchaff	Phylloscopus collybita
Coltsfoot	Tussilago farfara
Common blue butterfly	Polyommatus icarus
Common frog	Rana temporaria
Common spotted orchid	Dactylorrhiza fuchsii
Common tern	Sterna hirundo
Common vetch	Vicia sativa
Cowslip	Primula veris
Crocus	Crocus flavus
Daffodil	Narcissus pseudonarcissus
Damselfly	Calopteryx splendens
Dog rose	Rosa canina (also rosehip)

Early purple orchid	Orchis mascula
Elder	Sambucus nigra
Emperor moth	Saturnia pavonia
Fly agaric	Amanita muscaria
Fox	Vulpes vulpes
Fragrant orchid	Gymnadenia conopsea
Grayling butterfly	Hipparchia semele
Great-tit	Parus major
Greater butterfly orchid	Platanthera chlorantha
Green hairstreak butterfly	Callophrys rubi
Green woodpecker	Picus viridis
Harvest mouse	Micromys minutus
Hawthorn	Crataegus monogyna
Honeysuckle	Lonicera periclymenum
Horsechestnut	Aesculus hippocastanum
Horseshoe vetch	Hippocrepis comosa
Holly	Ilex aquifolium
Ivy	Hedera helix
Kingfisher	Alcedo atthis

List of Flora and Fauna

Kittiwake	*Rissa tridactylus*
Lapwing	*Vanellus vanellus*
Lesser celandine	*Ranunculus ficaria*
Long-tailed tit	*Aegithalos caudatus*
Marsh marigold	*Caltha palustris*
Marbled white butterfly	*Melanargia galathea*
Mistletoe	*Viscum album*
Orange tip butterfly	*Anthocharis cardamines*
Pearl-bordered fritillary butterfly	*Argynnis euphrosyne*
Pendunculate or English oak	*Quercus robur*
Primrose	*Primula vulgaris*
Pyramidal orchid	*Anacamptis pyramidalis*
Rabbit	*Oryctolagus cuniculus*
Red admiral butterfly	*Vanessa atalanta*
Red deer	*Cervus elaphus*
Robin	*Erithacus rubecula*
Rosehip	*Rosa canina (also dog rose)*
Sheep	*Ovis ammon*

Shelduck	*Tadorna tadorna*
Snowdrop	*Galanthus nivalis*
Snail	*Helix aspersa*
Shore crab	*Carcinus maenas*
Speckled wood butterfly	*Pararge aegeria*
Stinking hellebore	*Helleborus foetidus*
Stitchwort	*Stellaria holostea*
Stonechat	*Saxicola torquata*
Sundew	*Drosera rotundifolia*
Sycamore	*Acer pseudoplatanus*
Violet (sweet)	*Viola odorata*
White water lily	*Nymphaea alba*
Wild arum	*Arum maculatum*
Wild garlic	*Allium ursinum*
Winter aconite	*Eranthis hyemalis*
Wood mice	*Apodemus sylvaticus*
Wood sorrel	*Oxalis acetosella*
Yellow archangel	*Galeobdalon luteum*

Year Planner

January

April

February

May

March

June

Year Planner

July

October

August

November

September

December

Names and Addresses

Names and Addresses

Names and Addresses

Names and Addresses

Names and Addresses